Dedication:

To our first born, Saraiah lee.
Continue to let your light shine!!

Hi, my name is Saraiah, and today we are going to the park to meet some friends.

I love to wear my traditional African dress and bracelet called Lam, sent from my Godmother in Senegal.

I love going to the park to make new friends.

Mommy and Daddy say that I call everybody "my friends" even people that I do not know.

I walked up to a boy swinging all by himself on the saucer swing.

"HEY, FRIEND!"

His name is Beckham.

He loves to wear his hat when he goes
to the park, camping and fishing.
And now he's my friend.

Mommy lifted me up on the other side of the swing, and the two of us balanced each other out.

Our parents pushed us as we both went up and down while the wind swooshed in our faces.

Our laughter caught a girl's attention.

"Hey, Friend!"

Her name is Kiyoko.
She told us that she is wearing
her traditional Kimono dress and
Getas sandals.

Now she's our friend.

The three of us held on tightly while our parents
worked together to keep the swing balanced as
they spun us around and around.

We waved from afar, as another boy ran to the park,

"HEY, FRIEND!" we all shouted.

His name is Benjamin. He has on his Huarache sandals, Native Guayabera shirt, and gold bracelet that has been passed down as a part of their Mexican traditions.

Now he's our friend!

The four of us made the swing even more balanced.

LOOK OVER THERE!
We all noticed a little girl pulling her daddy towards us.

"HEY, FRIEND!"

Her name is Alohalani. She is wearing her Hawaiian Pa'u Hula Skirt and a lovely flower headpiece.

Now she's our friend.

The five of us are playing, laughing, and swinging in the wind. Alohalani brought even more steadiness to the swing!

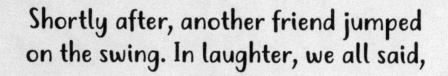

Shortly after, another friend jumped on the swing. In laughter, we all said,

"HEY, FRIEND!"

His name is Arya. He is wearing his traditional Kurta Pajama outfit.

Now he's our friend.

The six of us made the swing even
more steady and secure.

We have no worries or fears about anything because we are all soaring in unity.

I love playing with my friends at the park. Mommy and Daddy say that I call everyone "my friends."
Even people that I do not know.

And now our parents have new friends too!

I love my friends!

Dear readers,

We live in an era where we don't take the time to make new friends and embrace different cultures. This book is dear to us as it steps into the life of our 3 year old daughter Saraiah, who adores and calls everyone her friends!
The significance of this book is that the families illustrated are our actual friends and each one brings about the importance of unity. Our intent is not to offend or leave any group of people out but instead to lift up and embrace cultural differences and diversity.
The swing symbolizes life and the children sitting in it all play an important role in balancing the swing out.
We all play a part in helping the swing spin together.

CPSIA information can be obtained
at www.ICGtesting.com
Printed in the USA
BVHW011307210323
660849BV00024B/1120

9 780578 764993